Acting Scenes for Kids and Tweens

60 Original Comedy and Drama Scenes for Young Actors

Acting Scenes for Kids and Tweens

60 Original Comedy and Drama Scenes for Young Actors

Mike Kimmel

Foreword by Anita Barone

ISBN: 0998151300
ISBN 13: 9780998151304
Library of Congress Control Number: 2016915665
Ben Rose Creative Arts
New York-New Orleans

First edition

Praise for *Acting Scenes for Kids and Tweens*

"Great job, Mike! The scenes are well written, interesting, full of comedic touches and special insights. They play well and include valuable lessons. I like them all. They are an excellent collection for any youngster interested in honing their craft."
– William Wellman Jr.
Actor, Writer, and Producer
Wild Bill Wellman: Hollywood Rebel
    (Random House/Pantheon, 2015)
*The Man And His Wings: William A. Wellman and the
    Making of the First Best Picture* (Praeger)
Wild Bill Hollywood Maverick (Kino Classics)

"I have known Mike for a long time and I'm a big fan. In fact, I've hired him to star in a few of my films. But Mike's not just a great actor. He's also a born teacher. His latest book *Acting Scenes for Kids and Tweens*, is a must for young actors committed to enhancing their skills and mastering their talent. Most definitely a must have!"
– Suzanne Lyons
Producer, Snowfall Films
Undertaking Betty, The Calling, Jericho Mansions, Bailey's Billions, Portal, Séance, The Chaperone, Candy Stripers

"Mike Kimmel has created an invaluable resource for young actors. *Acting Scenes for Kids and Tweens* is a creative mix of comedy and drama. Mike makes it fun, and some scenes are educational, as well. Where was this book when I was teaching tweens acting back in the early 90s? From one Bronx Boy to another, well done Mike! Excellent follow up to your first book."

– John Duffy
Director & Producer
Duffy Square Productions
The Flag, Veterans Day, A Sunday Horse, Beneath the Darkness, Blood and Bone, Who's Your Caddy?

"Mike Kimmel's acting scenes for kids is a delightful collection of start-up scenes for young actors, scenes they can really play with! For these young actors, Kimmel's pieces are easily accessible and attractive to perform."

– Donald Brady
Professor of Drama
Loyola University
Actor, *Mississippi Grind, 99 Homes, Dallas Buyers Club, Leverage, Breakout Kings, A Love Song for Bobby Long, The Big Easy*

"I've had the pleasure of working with Mike in several films. He is a total professional – I loved working and collaborating with him. I've been an acting coach since 1995, and when he shared with me that he was going to start coaching, as well, I was very enthusiastic. He asked me where I got my scenes, and I told him 'I write them, and you should too.' And so he did! They are original, and are challenging emotionally and comedically without compromising the young actor's moral boundary with bad language and inappropriate situations. Mike has a wonderful sense of humor and knows comedic timing very well, in addition to being able to dig down deep into the depth of emotions and express it all through articulate scenes for young actors. So excited he's publishing his work!"

– Nancy Chartier
Nancy Chartier's Film Acting Studio

"*Acting Scenes for Kids and Tweens* is a treasure-trove for teachers, parents and students alike. As a long-time acting teacher and coach working primarily with young actors, I'm always searching for scenes with the right combination of humor, challenge and social relevance that will engage and challenge younger actors as they practice their acting skills for stage or screen. This delightful collection of original, age-appropriate scenes is a significant resource for my teaching! Thanks, Mike!"

– Sharon Garrison
Actor, Producer, and Acting Coach
Pitch Perfect 2, Salem, American Horror Story, Game of Silence
Portrayed Judge Amelia Sanders on *Drop Dead Diva* (AMC)

"A MUST buy book for any parent. Mike Kimmel's scenes are brilliantly written, a great way to challenge your acting skill, but most importantly they are fun! Whether you are just starting out in a showcase or looking to take your acting ability to the next level, *Acting Scenes for Kids and Tweens* is THE book to get!"
— Marco Bottiglieri
Writer, Director, and Producer
Happy Tree Films
Color Me You, The Absence, Truth Be Told, Custody, NoHo, A Soldier's Wife, Never Too Late

"Mike Kimmel has done it again! As with his first book, *Scenes for Teens,* the scenes here are well crafted and poignant, meticulously designed for kids in this age range. Whether for the classroom or performance, this book of scenes will hold its audience and hold its own. Bravo!"
— Joyce Storey
Founder
MonologuesToGo.com

"When I first came to the Big Apple, Mike Kimmel helped me out tremendously. He is a multi-talented actor/teacher and absolutely knows the "how to" of the business. Embrace this teacher and his book, *Acting Scenes for Kids and Tweens.* You will be better for it!"
— Teresa "Pie" Kline Truono
Miss Delaware USA 1994

"Coming from a librarian's perspective, I find that this book well fills the gap in any school or public library's collection on acting for children. It is an excellent source for modern day, 'real life' acting scenes for today's children, encompassing a range of emotions from jubilation to tragedy. Mike Kimmel's first book, *Scenes for Teens*, was exuberantly checked out by a young adult the very first day that I put it on display at my branch library. I expect no less enthusiasm and popularity from this latest book, *Acting Scenes for Kids and Tweens*."

– Linda Gielec, Librarian
Branch Manager, Children's Resource Center
New Orleans Public Library

"Mike Kimmel is one of the most generous actors I have ever met. He is willing to help people from all walks of life. If you are a kid or a parent who has children interested in acting you'll want to buy this book. The scenes Mike has written will give you material to start your training. You're never too young to start. Thank you, Mike Kimmel!"

– Ben McCain
TV Host, Actor, and Producer
My Name Is Bruce, Lois and Clark: The New Adventures of Superman, Bio-Dome, Martial Law, Black Scorpion, Nashville Now, Killer Tumbleweeds, Hee Haw

"*Acting Scenes for Kids and Tweens* is a great resource for young actors and teachers. The scenes are clean, educational, and funny. I wish I had this book when I was teaching kids!"

– Morgan Roberts
Actor, Writer, and Director
Temple, When the Game Stands Tall, Zoo, NCIS: New Orleans, American Horror Story, Ravenswood, The Inspectors

"In this, his second book, Mike Kimmel continues his investigation into creating short but durable scenes for young students, so that when they take on one of these remarkably efficient etudes, they can jumpstart (almost immediately) and therefore experience the dynamic of want vs. obstacle, which creates, of course, conflict: the essence of drama. What a boon this book will be to us arts educators, who welcome these kinds of tools for moving kids away from fear, distraction, boredom into choices that cut-to-the-guts."

– Dr. Henry Hoffman,
Artist/Teacher, New Orleans Center for Creative Arts
USA Today's All-USA Teacher Team
Director, Young Shakespeare Company

"*Acting Scenes for Kids and Tweens* is the perfect staple for every drama class. Kimmel has created an easy-to-use comedic and dramatic resource. As a vocal and drama coach, I appreciate the versatility of having a collection of age-appropriate scenes that are straightforward enough to work on cold reading exercises while still maintaining ample substance to delve into deeper scene study and character work."

– Misty Marshall
Actor, Director, and Teacher
Youth Performing Arts Director
American Idol: Season 2 Semifinalist

"Imagine kids & tweens learning lessons while doing what they love – acting? Brilliant! This scene book is like no other that I know of. It's smart, simple, inspirational, and teaches kids and tweens life lessons in a world that is bombarded with negative TV programming, bullying, peer pressure, bad language and way too much texting! A must-have for parents! Mike Kimmel's written words, once spoken, have the power to make kids and tweens not only better actors, but better human beings. Bravo!
   – Karen Ann Pavlick
   Actor, *Patch Adams, Nash Bridges, The Bold and the Beautiful,*
   HSN Host, NFL Oakland Raiders Cheerleader

"Another successfully executed book by the talented Mike Kimmel. The scenes are clever, witty and unique and totally accessible for a wide range of ages. I remember it being so hard when I was getting started in acting in New York City to find fantastic original material to work on and here in Mike's latest book there are so many wonderful choices! Wish this was available back then! I highly recommend this book for all young actors, teachers, and parents that want to support their kids on their journey into scene exploration."
   – Salli Saffioti
   Actor, Producer, Voiceover Artist
   Batman: Arkham Knight, Monster High, Marvel Super Hero Squad,
   Superman/Batman: Apocalypse, NYPD Blue, ER, In Plain Sight

"This is terrific training material for youngsters, and will prepare them well for the real world. It's always important to think ahead, even throughout your childhood. People who don't think of the future don't have one."
– "Judo" Gene LeBell
Legendary Stuntman, Grappler, and Martial Artist
Rocky, Raging Bull, Man on the Moon, L.A. Confidential, Spiderman 2, Batman & Robin, Independence Day, Liar Liar, Every Which Way But Loose, 24, The Fall Guy, The Munsters, The Beverly Hillbillies, Batman, The Adventures of Superman

"I think it's great that young people interested in performing on stage and screen will have this book to guide them. It's very important for kids to be encouraged and find solid, reputable mentors in their preferred fields. This book will do young actors a world of good."
– Johnny Valiant
Professional Wrestler, WWE Hall of Fame
Three-Time World Tag Team Champion

For Kimberley Bliquez and GiGi Erneta

"Do what you can, with what you have, where you are."

– Theodore Roosevelt

Table of Contents

Drama Scenes

Longer Scenes for Advanced Students

Shorter Scenes for Younger Actors

Foreword

You have to be lucky to make it in show business. Have you heard that one? Experts have been saying it for at least a hundred years. They'll tell you the actors you see on television and in the movies ... just got lucky.

Most actors I know who have paid their dues in the entertainment industry will not necessarily agree with that. Personally, though, I consider myself very lucky.

Let me tell you why. I figured out at five years old, in a St. Louis kindergarten class, that I wanted to be an actor. I played the witch in our production of *Annabelle Broom, The Unhappy Witch*, and knew in my heart that I had found my life's work. It wasn't just the applause. Honestly, I love the thrill of live performance. I love interacting with the audience. I loved it when I was in kindergarten, and I love it just as much today.

So I'm lucky because I always knew what I wanted to do. I'm lucky that my parents and teachers recognized my interest in the performing arts. I'm lucky they supported me.

I'm lucky they encouraged me to keep studying, practicing, and working hard to develop my craft.

Yes, I had to work hard. My parents worked hard too. They were incredibly resourceful, and did the best they could for all their children. While raising six other kids, they found time to help me pursue every local opportunity that was accessible and affordable. I took dance lessons, sang in the choir, and auditioned for every play I possibly could. I didn't always win the leading role. But every time

I was offered a supporting part, or even asked to play the understudy, I can promise you I literally jumped at the chance! I always enthusiastically said, "YES!" I wanted to keep studying, growing, and gaining experience. That was always the goal.

After building my credits locally, I made the move to Los Angeles in 1990. Just three days after my arrival, I lucked out again – with the opportunity of a lifetime. I was fortunate enough to be cast as a series regular in a new TV sketch comedy show alongside the legendary Carol Burnett, who still remains a hero and role model for me. Looking back, this was truly a breakthrough role, and the beginning of a long and fruitful career in television, film, and theater. I believe strongly in the old adage that luck is what happens for us when preparation meets opportunity. I also believe actors must take full responsibility for pursuing every available opportunity they can. Most of all, I believe I'm very lucky to still be living the life of my childhood dreams as a working actress in Hollywood.

If you're a young person who dreams of becoming an actor, I want to encourage you today. My advice is to give it everything you've got, and now you have a great book to help you practice and rehearse. I made the most of my resources, but I must say there was a decided lack of quality written material for young performers when I was your age. When I was growing up, I would have loved to be given this book of scenes Mike Kimmel has written for young kids. Today, I play the mom on TV shows with young kids, including *Shake It Up* on The Disney Channel. I also direct children in talent shows, workshops, and classes, so I'm thrilled to be part of this scene collection to help them work on acting fundamentals.

It's so important for actors to be honest and believable with one another on stage and screen. That's what *Acting Scenes for Kids and Tweens* is really all about. There's no need for extraneous props, costumes, or difficult staging instructions. You can just pick up the book and practice at home with your siblings. You can choose a favorite scene and practice it with your drama class at school. Whether or not you ultimately decide that acting is right for you, I know that getting up in front of people will build your confidence in any area you decide to pursue in life.

Congratulations to Mike for writing this book, and "good luck" to every young actor reading this! I hope you enjoy practicing these scenes, and I wish you the very best of everything.

Anita Barone
Los Angeles, California

Acknowledgments

A million thanks to my three wonderful sisters Mollie, Adele, and Tammy for always being there for me.

Many thanks to Lauren Alexandra, Kimberley Bliquez, GiGi Erneta, Sharon Garrison, Tina Guillot, Misty Marshall, Judy Stecher, Jan Sutton, Grissel Villar, David Breland, Dr. Henry Hoffman, Morgan Roberts, Dr. David Samadi, Ray Weber, and William Wellman Jr. for providing mountains of support, encouragement, and thoughtful advice.

And last, but certainly not least, very special thanks to the one and only Anita Barone for sharing so generously of her time, talent, and insights. Anita is one of those rare, extraordinary performers who make Hollywood shine even brighter for all the world.

Introduction

I'm proud of you.

A lot of kids say they want to perform on stage and screen but never actually do anything about it. Many children don't have access to arts programs in their local communities and don't know where to begin. Some others, unfortunately, may not yet be motivated to train and develop their skills. But acting is just like any other field of study. It requires a great deal of dedication and hard work before you begin to see positive results.

If you're a youngster picking up this book, you're demonstrating discipline and respect for the craft and the business of acting. Those are very admirable qualities for young performers and will benefit you in every area of your life. Acting requires a great deal of preparation, planning, and concentration. When we see actors (of any age) delivering strong, memorable performances in television, film, and theater, we should always remember these performances grew out of focus, daily practice, and dedication. It's also extremely important to have patience with ourselves as we study diligently to develop these qualities.

I've known from an early age that I wanted to perform on stage and screen, write books and scripts, and tell stories. When I was a young boy growing up in the Bronx, New York, I honestly could not figure out how to get started. I also couldn't find anyone to point me in the right direction. There were no acting classes for children in my area at that time, and my family didn't know anyone in the entertainment industry to guide us.

I would have loved to get my hands on a book of simple and straightforward scenes to practice realistic dialogue for stage and screen.

I've now had the opportunity to train and perform as an actor in New York, Los Angeles, and throughout the United States. In that time, I've met many other actors and acting coaches whose early experiences were remarkably similar to my own. As children, they looked for guidance and practical material to help them get started in acting. Many never found the resources they needed. Like myself, they gravitated towards other fields and areas of interest. Sure, we *eventually* got started in show business, but it wasn't until somewhat later in life. We never had the experience of performing as child actors.

That's the main reason behind *Acting Scenes for Kids and Tweens.* These sixty original short scripts are written for two actors, allowing young people to simply grab a friend and start practicing. With this book, the focus is on creating conversational, realistic dialogue between young performers. Consequently, there are no additional characters cluttering up the scenes. There are no entrances or exits. Actors also do not need to concern themselves with costumes, props, or stage directions. All they need is focus, discipline, and a dedicated scene partner.

The scripts are gender-neutral, as well. That means every character in every scene can be either male or female. No need to search for a girl-boy, boy-boy, or girl-girl scene. Every young actor who picks up this book can practice every role in every scene. To simplify the process further, characters are simply called "A and B" rather than given traditional male and female names. This also makes it easier to switch roles and practice both parts, a valuable exercise used regularly by experienced actors.

Remember that an actor's job is to pretend to be someone else. We have to accomplish this as realistically as possible.

Realism is always our goal. It has to look like the characters in a comedy or drama are really talking to each other in a natural and conversational style. That's what we're always striving for as actors. Believe me, this is not as easy as it looks. We must read and memorize words someone we've never met has written for us. Then we have to convince an audience of other strangers that we were thinking these words up in our own minds – and speaking them out of our own mouths – for the very first time. The scenes in this book are intended to help young people practice and deliver lines of dialogue simply and realistically. The style and format is modeled after my earlier book, *Scenes for Teens.* The overall goal for both books is to simplify and demystify the process for young performers.

It has been a pleasure and a privilege to create this book of comedy and drama scenes for young people. I hope boys and girls will enjoy the process of working on these scripts and that the experience will bring them one step closer to achieving their goals.

Additionally, I hope teachers will find this book useful in coaching student actors and preparing them to win amateur and professional roles on stage and screen. Parents, grandparents, aunts, and uncles may also enjoy practicing with the kids to make acting a fun, productive, and rewarding activity for the entire family.

Thank you for selecting this book. If you will take the time to practice these scenes daily – even for twenty or thirty minutes – I think you will be amazed at the progress you will make, the skills you will develop, and the confidence you will build as young actors. And amazement is a worthy goal for every one of us to work towards.

The best actors I've met always seem to be the hardest working, as well. Nobody can tell me that's a coincidence. I agree wholeheartedly with what Anita Barone says – the harder we work, the luckier we become. We all have a far greater capacity for hard work and achievement than we think we do. Keep training, studying, and moving forward. And always remember to have fun. You can work hard at something and still find a way to make it fun. I wish you all the very best on this exciting new journey you have chosen.

Mike Kimmel
New Orleans, Louisiana

A Note for Teachers

Some of these scenes are whimsical, while others are meant to give your students something a bit deeper to think about. Some are specifically written to help young actors develop rapid-fire comedic timing. Others, though, will be more appropriate for working on subtext, vocal variety, and silent reactions to the other character's lines of dialogue. There are a few positive, uplifting messages sprinkled throughout, as well. Most actors respond well to a strategically placed encouraging word.

All in all, the intent is to provide a variety of material to work with, so that students will remain interested and engaged from week to week. It's always useful to switch things up, going from comedy to drama, silly to serious, shorter to longer, to present young actors with a wide range of styles and challenges. This approach will be especially valuable for your more serious and dedicated students – those interested in auditioning for professional projects. Ideally, actors should be equally comfortable with comedy and drama. As educators, it's our responsibility to help young actors become fluid, flexible, and creative in their thinking, as well. I believe you will find this a practical and effective strategy to prepare your students for the many different scenarios they will encounter in the audition room.

Comedy Scenes

My Summer Vacation

A Did your teacher give you that same old, same old home-work assignment?

B Do you mean –

A My summer vacation! I hate my summer vacation!

B But you said you had a good vacation!

A I did! I had a great vacation! I just don't like writing about it!

B Why? It's such an easy assignment.

A Exactly! I don't want an easy homework assignment! Why do our teachers give us that same assignment every year?

B Maybe they have to. Maybe the school makes them do it.

A You mean it's like a part of their job?

B It has to be. That must be why so many different teach-ers assign it every year.

A I wonder what our teachers do on *their* summer vacation?

B Probably sit around, eat cheeseburgers, and think up new ways to be mean to us kids.

A Sounds pretty boring if you ask me.

B No wonder they're so interested in *our* summer vacation!

A Synonym for Penmanship

A I need help with my school work. How is your penmanship?

B What kind of a ship?

A Penmanship.

B What's penmanship?

A That's a big, fancy word for handwriting.

B Why don't they just call it handwriting?

A I don't know. Maybe penmanship sounds more serious.

B I guess so. So they're synonyms?

A What's a synonym?

B Two words that mean the same thing.

A So penmanship is a synonym for handwriting?

B I think so.

A Is there another word for synonym?

B I'm not sure. But your penmanship is starting to give me a headache.

A Is there a synonym for headache?

B I don't know. Is there a synonym for annoying?

I'm Afraid of Pizza

A   Can I tell you a secret?

B   Sure. I can keep a secret.

A   I'm afraid of pizza ...

B   What?

A   I said I'm afraid of pizza!

B   But pizza can't hurt you! Pizza is good, and nice, and friendly.

A   No! Pizza is extremely dangerous!

B   How can pizza be dangerous?

A   A slice of pizza has a sharp point like a knife! It can stab you!

B   Maybe it's pointy, but it's not sharp!

A   And pizza can be very hot! It can burn you!

B   But you can have round pizza, like a little mini-pizza. Round pizza doesn't have a sharp point.

A   It's still hot.

B   You can eat cold pizza. My Grandpa Bob eats cold pizza all the time. He says cold pizza is delicious.

A   It's still scary.

B   Don't be afraid. Pizza was invented to help us. You have to make friends with pizza.

Get Off The Phone

A Will you do me a favor?

B I guess. What is it?

A Will you put away your phone?

B Yeah, okay. Just a minute.

A Come on. Put it away. I'm trying to talk with you.

B Just a second. I have to finish sending this text.

A Excuse me! Excuse me! Will you please put that away? I'm trying to have a human being conversation with you!

B What is your problem today?! I'm sitting right here with you, and we're having a conversation!

A You're talking, but you're not even looking at me. You're looking at your phone.

B I can do two things together at the same time.

A But I have something important to tell you.

B What?

A I have something very important to talk with you about.

B Uh ... yeah, okay. Go ahead. I'm listening.

A Never mind ... I'll send you a text.

B Huh? What did you say?

My Trip to New Zealand

A You look happy.

B I am! I'm going to New Zealand!

A When?

B I don't know. I just decided this morning. We learned about it in school.

A Cool. Where is New Zealand anyway?

B I'm not exactly sure.

A Then why do you want to go there?

B It's supposed to be so beautiful nobody ever wants to leave.

A That sounds great! Why don't we look it up on a map?

B Good idea. I think my teacher said it's somewhere near Australia.

A Nice. Do they have kangaroos there too?

B No, I don't think so.

A Why not?

B I don't know. Maybe it's too far to hop all the way from Australia to New Zealand.

A Well, I think that's a shame. A crying shame.

B But the good news is they have more different kinds of penguins in New Zealand than any other country.

A More kinds of penguins?

B That's what they tell me. All different kinds of penguins.

A Sign me up! I'm going to New Zealand with you!

Walking My Dog

A Are you allowed to walk your dog?

B No, my parents say I'm too little.

A Me too! I think it stinks!

B Yeah! If I'm old enough to play with him, I should be able to walk him!

A I know! I told my dad I want to start helping out at home.

B What did he say?

A He said it's not much help to anybody if the dog is dragging me down the street like a bag of macaroni.

B But your dog isn't even that big!

A I know, but he pulls really hard.

B Yeah, mine pulls really hard too! I think it has to do with their breed.

A Maybe that's why our folks won't let us walk them by ourselves.

B You're probably right. We'll just have to wait until we get older.

A I guess so.

B Yeah. It's too bad Chihuahuas pull so hard.

A I know!

B I guess they have a lot to prove!

Turn Off The Moon

A What's the matter with you?

B Nothing. Nothing, nothing nothing!

A Looks like something. What's bothering you?

B The stupid moon.

A The moon? How could the moon be bothering you?

B Because it's always shining! Last three nights it's so big and bright, it shines through my window all night long!

A Well, it's been a full moon the last couple of nights.

B You're telling me! Turn that thing off for a couple of hours! I can't get any sleep!

A You can't turn off the moon! It's so beautiful. That's why they write songs about the moon and the moonlight.

B Well, I'm not singing any of them. I'm sick and tired of the moon. I don't even think it's real.

A Of course it's real! The moon is part of our solar system.

B I don't care. Who needs it?

A Everybody needs it! It's good for the tides and the oceans and all kinds of other stuff.

B Well, it isn't any good for me. I'm un-friending the moon.

How Are You?

A How are you doing?

B Fantastic, but I'm gonna get better!

A Really? That good?

B Yeah! Great! Never better!

A Wow! What's so good?

B Everything! The sun is shining. The birds are singing. The cupcakes are baking.

A Are you just trying to be silly?

B Not silly. Happy. I appreciate everything.

A What do you appreciate?

B I'm alive. I have a great family. Great friends. I appreciate you for being my friend.

A Don't you worry about school, and growing up, and all that scary stuff?

B Nope. Not at all.

A How about the horrible weather?

B What's so horrible about it?

A It's raining again.

B That's good. Rain makes the flowers grow.

I Like Everything!

A My mom keeps telling me I need to eat more fruits and veggies.

B My favorite foods. Natural colors. Natural flavors.

A But I can't decide which ones to pick. Do you like carrots?

B Yeah, they're supposed to be good for your eyes.

A How do you know that?

B Well, did you ever see a rabbit wearing glasses?

A That's pretty funny.

B I like broccoli too.

A Yuck-O! Not me!

B Broccoli's good for your hair, teeth, tongue, and toenails.

A But it's so ugly and fluffy. It's like eating a tree!

B Trees are great! I love trees! I love all kinds of plants and flowers and trees and vegetables!

A I gotta pick out fruit too. Do you like fruit?

B Oh, yeah! Fruit's delicious! How about you?

A Well … I like some kinds of fruit, but not the ones with a lot of disgusting, sticky little seeds that get caught between my teeth.

B I love disgusting, sticky little seeds that get caught between my teeth!

A That's crazy! Nobody likes those horrible, disgusting kinds of seeds!

B I do! I like everything!

The Cheeseburger Museum

A Guess what? My class is going on a field trip tomorrow.

B Where?

A To the museum.

B Which one?

A I don't know. How many different ones are there?

B There are all different kinds. They have art museums and history museums and dinosaur bone museums.

A Oh. I never thought about it before. I didn't realize there were so many.

B They even have an alligator museum.

A What kind of people would go to an alligator museum?

B I don't know. People who want to learn about alligators and crocodiles and snakes and reptiles and stuff.

A Count me out.

B I heard a lot of people eat alligators.

A That's disgusting!

B Maybe to you and me. But it's probably normal for people who grew up around all kinds of alligators.

A I grew up around all kinds of cheeseburgers.

B Maybe they have a cheeseburger museum somewhere.

A Maybe that's where my class is going tomorrow.

B Maybe you're taking me with you.

We Need More Exercise!

A Come on. Let's play a video game.

B Nah. I want to go outside and play.

A I thought you liked video games.

B Sometimes, but I want to play something real – not fake.

A Video games are real. Real expensive.

B I mean we have to get more exercise!

A Maybe you should join a gym.

B I'm not sure kids are allowed.

A Why not?

B I think you have to be eighteen.

A That's not fair.

B Yes, it is. Because we're supposed to run around outside and play. That's how us kids are supposed to get our exercise.

A I want to get my exercise playing video games.

B That's not good exercise.

A Sure it is. It's good exercise for my fingers and my eyeballs.

B I think we gotta get you to the playground, my friend. Fingers, eyeballs, and all the rest of you too.

The Oddly Obscure Ocelot

A How do you spell ocelot?

B Spell what?

A Ocelot.

B I don't know. I'd have to think a lot.

A Good. Think up how to spell it for me.

B What is it? A store?

A Animal. Some kind of wild creature.

B Sorry. I never even heard of such an animal, and I don't know how to spell it.

A Can you look it up?

B Why don't you look it up?

A Because I don't know how to spell it

B I don't know how to spell it, either. I don't even think it's real.

A It's definitely real, and it's a very important animal.

B Are you making all this up?

A No! I'm telling you that you have to help me! This is an important animal.

B Might be a good idea to learn how he spells his name.

Memorize the Presidents

A Do you know any good jokes?

B No, but I have a riddle.

A Works for me.

B Which American President wore the biggest hat?

A Easy! Abraham Lincoln!

B No. The one with the biggest head!

A Ohhhh …that's sneaky!

B I know. Everyone wants to say Lincoln.

A Yeah, because he wore a tall hat.

B A stove pipe hat.

A Uh-huh. But I guess … that doesn't make it the biggest, right?

B Exactly.

A What else do you know about Abraham Lincoln?

B I know he was sixteenth President.

A How do you remember that?!

B Because I memorized them.

A That's amazing! You memorized all the Presidents?!

B Well … I didn't exactly finish …

A What do you mean you didn't finish?

B I'm still working on it. So for starters, I just memorized the good ones.

Who Was That?

A   Hello again.

B   Hi. Hi. Hi.

A   Are you still waiting for Susan?

B   She should be here soon ...

A   Susan?

B   Sue.

A   Who?

B   Your cousin Susan.

A   She's not my cousin! I thought she was your cousin!

B   My cousin Susan from California?

A   No! Your cousin Sue from Ohio.

B   No. I would never wait for her.

A   Me neither.

B   Good.

A   Hey! Don't talk that way about my cousin!

B   She's my cousin too, you know!

A   Well ... she was my cousin first!

B   Doesn't matter. I've been waiting for her longer!

What Do You Want To Be When You Grow Up?

A What do you want to be when you grow up?

B Taller!

A That's funny!

B I'm serious! I want to be really tall!

A You mean like a basketball player?

B Taller! I mean like a giant!

A But giants aren't even real.

B How do you know?

A Because I've never seen one.

B That's because you've never been to Scotland.

A They have giants in Scotland?

B They have everything in Scotland.

A Okay. Then I want to be taller too.

B You want to be a giant with me?

A No. I want to be even taller than a giant!

B There's nothing taller than a giant.

A Yes, there is! We just can't see them from where we are now!

B I wonder if we can see them from Scotland.

Drama Scenes

The Bus

A Will you sit with me on the bus?

B Sure. Why?

A Because I haven't made any new friends here yet. I don't know anybody else at school.

B That's no biggie. You just meet people.

A But it's hard.

B Only in the beginning.

A The beginning of what?

B The beginning of anything.

A But how do you start? How do you meet new people in a new school?

B I don't know. But I don't think anybody knows. You just talk to them. Like you started talking to me.

A But what if they don't like me? What if they're mean?

B Well ... I guess that could happen, but then you just talk to someone else.

A I don't know. A lot of people are just not that friendly ...

B Not everyone's going to be nice, but not everyone's going to be mean either. I think there's gonna be plenty of nice kids riding that bus.

A But how do you know that?

B You're a nice kid, and you're gonna be riding that bus.

My Teacher Said a Bad Word!

A What's wrong?

B Nothing … I'm okay …

A No, you're not. You look upset.

B Uh … a little … maybe a little. Something weird happened in school today.

A What happened?

B My teacher said a really bad word.

A What word?

B I don't want to repeat it. I'm not allowed. But it's a very bad word that they say in the movies sometimes.

A Why did your teacher say it? Was she talking about a movie?

B No. She was yelling and screaming at two of the kids.

A Did you tell your mom and dad?

B No.

A I think you should tell your mom and dad.

B I don't want to start any trouble.

A I'm pretty sure teachers are not supposed to yell at the kids. And they're definitely not supposed to say bad words.

Can I Copy Your Homework?

A Did you finish all your homework?

B Sure. I always do my homework.

A Great! Can I see it?

B Why?

A So I can copy it.

B No!

A Don't worry. I'll change it a little.

B What do you mean?

A You won't get in trouble. I'll change it so nobody will know I copied it.

B But I'll know you copied it.

A So? Who cares? You're my friend.

B Uh-huh. Friends don't ask friends to cheat.

A Yeah, right! Grow up!

B I am grown up.

A Doesn't look like it.

B I did my homework too. I did *my own* homework. Like a grown-up! You should try it sometime!

A You are being so rude today.

B A lot of grown-ups are rude.

What Do You Like To Read?

A What did you get for your birthday?

B A brand new book!

A That kinda stinks.

B It's kinda great. I love to read.

A Not me. I think books are boring.

B Well, it all depends. What kind of books do you have?

A I have all kinds of story books and kids' books.

B With pictures?

A Of course with pictures.

B That's the problem right there.

A Why?

B Your books are too baby-fied. They're too easy for you.

A You think so?

B Definitely. You need big, thick books to read and study. Like grown-ups get. Look for something with a table of contents. No pictures.

A Well … I guess that would make it more of a challenge.

B Yeah, you'd get a lot more good information in an adult book. Let's go to the library and I'll help you find one. What kind of a book would you be interested in?

A Do they have any with puffy stickers?

I Have to Help My Mom …
With Her Homework!

A You want to watch a movie with me?

B No. I have to help my mom with her homework.

A You mean she has to help you with *your* homework.

B No. My mom has *her* homework.

A That's dumb. How can your mom have homework? Is she being punished because you don't do *your* homework?

B No, she has her own homework. She went back to school a little while ago.

A What grade is she in?

B No kind of grade. She's in college.

A Didn't she go to college a long time ago? I thought I saw pictures.

B Yeah. She went to college with my dad. Then she had to stop when they had me.

A So now she wants to finish?

B Right. Mom says you're never too old to learn something new.

A I guess you're never too young either.

B Right again. We can all just keep getting better, and keep learning, and keep getting smarter, and keep doing all kinds of good stuff.

A Sounds pretty good to me.

B See that? You're getting smarter already.

Summer Plans with Grandma and Grandpa

A Are you going to camp this summer?

B No. I think I'm gonna visit my grandma and grandpa in the country instead.

A That's too bad.

B No, it's not. My grandparents are awesome.

A Yeah, but there's no kids for you to hang around with there.

B I'm not going to hang around with kids. I'm going to hang out with my grandma and grandpa.

A Are your parents making you?

B Well ... no, actually. It's my idea.

A Don't you think that's a little weird?

B No. They're getting older, and I want to spend as much time with them as I can.

A How old are they?

B I'm not exactly sure. But a couple of kids in my class lost their grandparents this year, and it made me think how much I would miss mine if I didn't have them to visit any more.

A Okay, I guess I never thought about it like that.

B Yeah, so I told my mom and dad that's what I want to do this summer.

Pretty Little Pageant Princess

A Is your sister really doing that dumb beauty pageant?

B It's not dumb. She's really excited about it.

A Isn't she a little young for a beauty pageant?

B Not really. They have a Little Miss category. That's the one she's in.

A Isn't it kind of stupid and old-fashioned, though?

B Honestly, that's what I thought too. But you wouldn't believe how much it's helped her.

A Helped her how? Teaching her how to walk? How to wave?

B Since she started practicing for this pageant, she's like a whole new kid. She's super polite. Her grades have improved. She does all her homework now. It's unbelievable.

A You're right. I don't believe it.

B I didn't believe it either. But she even *looks* happier now.

A All that from a pageant?

B I think it's because they set goals.

A Then they reach them?

B Well … not always. We can't win at everything.

A But working at it is good for her self-esteem, you mean?

B It's good for my self-esteem! Now I've got the coolest little sister in the whole world!

How Grown-Ups Don't Think

A Tell me something.

B No.

A Why do people smoke?

B Why do they smoke cigarettes?

A Yeah, cigarettes.

B I don't know. Maybe they like it.

A How can they like it? It's disgusting.

B Maybe not to them.

A Well, it is to me. I was driving with my dad, and I started smelling cigarette smoke.

B I didn't know your dad smokes.

A He doesn't! It was coming from another car.

B Another driver?

A Yeah. This lady in another car was smoking, but she was stretching her arm all the way out the window like *this*! So she didn't have to smell it herself!

B That's weird. Maybe the smoke bothers her. Maybe she doesn't wanna stink up her car.

A Duh. Then maybe she shouldn't smoke.

B Well ... maybe that's how grown-ups think.

A No. Maybe that's how grown-ups *don't* think.

Smart Braces

A Want to go swimming?

B No. I have to go to the dentist.

A Again? Didn't you just go last week?

B Yeah. She has to work on my stupid braces some more.

A Oh, come on. Don't say it like that.

B My stupid braces. My stupid braces. I hate my stupid, stupid braces.

A Someday, you'll love those braces.

B Yeah, right.

A I mean it. My Aunt Dana had braces when she was our age.

B Your Aunt Dana? She's the pretty one, right?

A They're all pretty.

B I didn't know she had braces.

A Yeah. So did my dad and my Uncle David.

B But they all have such good, straight teeth. Such nice smiles.

A Yeah, because they went to the dentist a hundred million times.

B Okay. I'm not going to the dentist to fix my stupid braces anymore.

A You're not?

B No. I'm going to the dentist so she can fix my *smart braces*.

My Overprotective Father

A Ooooo! Look at that motorcycle!

B Yeah? So what?

A Don't you like motorcycles?

B Not really. My dad says they're too dangerous.

A Your dad says everything is too dangerous!

B He's just trying to be a good father.

A Yeah, but that doesn't help. He's overprotective!

B No. He just wants to take good care of us. Keep us all safe.

A But we're not little kids anymore. Your dad can't protect you from everything.

B Well ... he's not trying to protect me from everything. Just dangerous stuff.

A But how are we gonna grow up? How are we gonna learn anything if we don't try new stuff?

B Learning stuff is fine. I love learning new stuff. I think my dad just wants to know I'm not learning stuff that's gonna keep him up all night worrying about me!

A You know what you sound like?

B No, but I have a funny feeling you're gonna tell me.

A I am gonna tell you. You sound like some kinda old person.

B Well ... how do you think old people get to be old people?

The New Babysitter

A Can you come over and study with me tonight?

B Can't. I have to stay home.

A Why?

B My parents are going out, and I'm not allowed to leave. We have a babysitter for me and my brother.

A Cool. Who's your babysitter? Lisa?

B No. We have a different babysitter now.

A Is she nice?

B Uh … I don't know … she's okay …

A What do you mean "okay?"

B I guess she's all right … uh … but she doesn't talk so nice to us …

A Did you tell your parents?

B No … not really …

A Why not?

B I don't want to be a tattle-tale.

A I think you're making a big mistake.

B Yeah? Why?

A Any time a grown-up isn't nice to us, we're supposed to tell our parents.

B But she's not really a grown-up yet. She's just a teenager.

A You still have to tell your parents.

All My Old Toys

A Do you have any old toys?

B Sure. I have old toys and new toys. Why?

A Can I have them?

B What for?

A I'm getting rid of all my old toys. And toys I don't play with anymore.

B What are you gonna do with them? You're not just gonna throw them away, are you?

A No. I'm bringing them over to donate them.

B Donate them where?

A This place that my mom found. It's a shelter.

B Like a bus shelter? A shelter from the rain?

A No, a different kind. It's like a home for people who don't have a regular place to live. There are kids there too.

B You mean like homeless kids?

A I think so. My mom had the idea that we can give them toys me and my sisters don't play with anymore.

B I think that's a really good thing. I can give you some of my old toys too.

A Great! Thanks very much.

B How about clothes? Do those kids need any clothes?

A I don't know! Probably! Never thought about the clothes!

B Well, let's collect some! Maybe they need clothes too!

Longer Scenes
for Advanced Students

Big Sisters Are Very Special People!

A Are you going to Gabriella's party?

B Gabriella Rose?

A Yeah. Her mom and dad are giving her a big party.

B Cool. I didn't know it's her birthday.

A It's not. Her birthday is in May.

B So what's the party for?

A It's a big sister party.

B A what?

A A big sister party.

B What's that?

A Just what it sounds like. It's a party for big sisters.

B Really?

A Yeah. Because her mom and dad say she helps out so much at home. She helps her parents with her little brother and sister.

B Oh, those twins are so cute!

A Adorable! Little Dylan and Julianna! And Gabby always helps watch them.

B She's such a sweet girl!

A I know! I love Gabriella!

B Everyone does. She's always so nice to everybody.

A Yep. Sure is. She's teaching her cousin Madison now. Showing Madison how to help with her baby brother Max.

B Ooooh! I love Madison and Max!

A The M and M team!

B Awesome. Gabriella's one of my favorite kids at school. Best in the West.

A That's why her parents are giving her a big sister party. Big sisters are very special people.

B You can say that again.

A Okay. Big sisters are very special people.

The Best Birthday Party Ever

A Are you coming to my birthday party Saturday?

B. Yeah, definitely!

A. Great.

B Are you having a balloon bounce?

A Nah, my mom thinks they 're dangerous.

B Are you having a magician?

A Nah..... My dad says it's too expensive for us right now. Besides, everybody does that nowadays.

B Okay. Are you going to have a clown?

A No. My little brother is afraid of clowns.

B So what are you having?

A My parents said they want me to have an old-fashioned birthday party like they had when they were my age.

B Cool. What are you having?

A Just a big, giant chocolate cake and some funny birthday party hats!

B Really?! That's all you're having?!

A Nope. I'm having one more thing. The most important thing.

B What?

A I'm having all my super-awesome friends! That's the best part of all!!

B. This sounds like a weird party! It's so different from the big fancy birthday parties all the other kids have!

A   Exactly. So you're gonna be there, right?

B. Yeah. Definitely. I wouldn't miss it!

A   Great.

B   Looking forward to that big, giant chocolate cake, my friend.

A   Glad to hear it.

B   Glad to say it.

A   Glad to share it.

B   Glad to eat it.

Canadian Mother's Day

A Wanna come over my house?

B Can't. We're having a special dinner. It's Mother's Day.

A No, it's not. Mother's Day is in May.

B I know, but my mom says it's Canadian Mother's Day.

A That's kinda weird. I never heard of that.

B I didn't either, but my mom says it's today. She also told me that Canadian Mother's Day is not just one day. It lasts from now until New Year's Eve.

A But ... but that's months! You can't have a holiday that lasts months!

B They do in Canada.

A Why? Because it's so cold?

B Probably. And all the kids have to be super-duper, extra nice to their moms.

A Nicer than kids in other countries have to behave?

B Much nicer. It used to be twice as nice as all the other countries. But Canada just changed the rule. Now kids have to be three times as nice.

A Three times as nice?!

B Yep. Thrice.

A All the way until the end of the year?!

B Uh-huh. That's the rule.

A But maybe that rule is just for Canadian kids.

B Yeah, that's what I thought. But my mom said that if a kid from another country finds out about it ... that kid has to follow the Canadian rule too.

A That sounds like a lot of crazy rules over at your house!

B Tell me about it! My dad says Australian Father's Day starts tomorrow!

Thanksgiving Every Month

A What's your favorite holiday?

B I don't know. Why?

A My Grandma Rose always says Thanksgiving is her favorite holiday.

B Why? Because she likes turkey?

A Sure, but not just that. She says it's really important to be grateful for all the good things we have.

B Okay. I guess that makes sense.

A Grandma Rose says it's the best holiday. And we live in the best country. And we have to make sure we appreciate it every day and always give thanks.

B I guess I never thought about it like that.

A That's why she says Thanksgiving is the most important holiday. And it's too bad it only comes once a year.

B But every holiday comes once a year.

A My Grandma Rose says Thanksgiving is so special … we should have it every month.

B Thanksgiving every month?!

A Yeah. Why not? I bet a lot of people would like to have Thanksgiving every month.

B Maybe a lot of people. But I think the turkeys might not like it too much.

A That's pretty funny!

B Thank you.

A   Thank you! I'm thankful for your sense of humor!

B   Thank you again!

A   And I'm thankful for your friendship.

B   I'm thankful for *your* friendship!

A   And I'm thankful we have the holiday of Thanksgiving.

B   And ... I'm thankful you're so thankful.

A   Thank you.

B   You're welcome.

A   Thank you for saying "You're welcome."

B   You're welcome.

You're Special

A Got a minute?

B Sure. What's up?

A I have to tell you a secret.

B Okay.

A I'm invisible.

B What?

A I said I'm invisible.

B No, you're not. I'm looking right at you.

A But you're the only one who can see me.

B Stop talking weird.

A You can see me because you have super powers.

B Come on. Cut it out.

A I'm serious. It's because you're special.

B That's funny.

A It is?

B It is. You sound like my mom.

A I do?

B You do. You know what my mom always says?

A No. I can't read minds. I don't have that power.

B She says, "You're special and unique – just like everyone
   else!"

A Wow! That's ... brilliant!

B Yeah. My mom's super smart.

A Is she invisible too?

B No. I see her every day.

A You do?

B I do.

A See? That's because you're special.

It Was All Mush

A Did you ever go to an art museum?

B I don't think so. I only went to the museum with the dinosaur fossils. Why?

A My mom and dad took me yesterday.

B Did you like it?

A Not too much. The artwork was kind of ... I don't know ...

B Any nice paintings?

A There were a lot of *big* paintings. They had statues too. But they weren't all that nice.

B Maybe it's a bunch of new artists and they don't have too much experience yet.

A No. The artists weren't new. They were just confusing! I didn't understand the pictures.

B How can you not understand? They're just pictures of people's faces, right?

A No! That's the problem! I understand those. These were paintings that didn't make any kind of sense. They were all mush!

B Any pictures of flowers or trees or fruit?

A No. They were pictures of nothing. Just mush.

B What do you mean when you say "mush?"

A I don't know. Just mush. A big mushy kind of a mush.

B Oh, now I get it. That's modern art! My parents have books about that mush.

A   There was only one picture I liked in the whole museum.

B   What was it?

A   A bunch of squiggly lines.

B   But how could you like it if it's just wiggly lines?

A   Because it reminds me of my favorite toy when I was a little kid. My Etch a Sketch!

B   Ooooh! I love Etch a Sketch! I want to go to the Mush Museum!

Bananas for Bananas!

A Are you still hungry?

B Yeah! Do you have any bananas?

A Bananas again? Why do you always want to eat a banana?

B It's my most favorite food.

A Yuck- O!!

B I love bananas. I eat one or two every day.

A They're so squishy and smelly and mushy. Don't you ever get tired of them?

B Never!

A There's plenty of other good fruits and vegetables.

B I know. I eat all different kinds. But bananas are my favorite.

A What's so good about them?

B They've got all kinds of vitamins that are good for us. And a ton of potassium.

A What's potassium?

B It's a mineral. Our bodies need those too.

A So I guess you're telling me bananas are really healthy for us, right?

B Plus they're delicious! You should have a banana with me right now!

A How about a banana split? I wouldn't mind having one of those ...

B Well the banana part is good for us, but … uh … I don't know about the split …

A You know what I think?

B Not yet …

A I think you're bananas for bananas!

B Thanks! It's the healthy way to be!

Chocolate Covered Chocolate
with Chocolate Chips

A Are you going to the bake sale?

B No, my mom doesn't like us eating that sugary stuff.

A Too bad. I love dessert. My most favorite thing.

B Not good for us, though.

A Tastes great. Yummy, yummy in my tummy.

B I know, but my mom says it gives us a sugar rush. Then we get tired later on and fizzle out.

A I like chocolate best.

B And my little brother's allergic to chocolate. So we never even have it at home.

A Allergic to chocolate? I don't know what I'd do if I was allergic to chocolate. I'd have to move to Alaska or something.

B It's not so bad. If you don't have it at home, you don't think about it. And then you don't miss it. And Alaska's supposed to be beautiful, by the way.

A Not without chocolate, it's not.

B I'm sure they've got great chocolate in the great state of Alaska.

A Do you think they have great bake sales?

B I wouldn't be at all surprised.

A I'm going to our bake sale early. I want to be the first one there. So I can check out all the tables.

B What's your favorite?

A I told you. Anything with chocolate.

B Oh, that's right.

A Or even chocolate chips.

B Okay. That makes sense.

A Sometimes you can get a giant chocolate cookie ... with chocolate chips.

B Sounds pretty ... chocolatey.

A Maybe a chocolate muffin with chocolate chips.

B I bet they have those too.

A Or just a plain chocolate bar.

B Sounds good.

A Even better with chocolate chips.

B Sounds like a festival of chocolate.

A And maybe they can dip the whole thing in chocolate.

B To give it a hard chocolate shell?

A Yeah... then I can have chocolate covered chocolate with chocolate chips.

I'm Bored ...

A I'm bored ...

B Wanna play tic tac toe?

A No, that's dumb. Baby game.

B Wanna play cards?

A No, that's boring. Cards are for old people.

B Cards are for everybody.

A Everybody old and boring.

B Wanna go for a walk?

A Where to?

B I don't know. Maybe the park. Get some fresh air?

A Why? So we can walk all around the park in circles and look at a bunch of stupid trees?

B No. So we can get a little exercise.

A I'll pass.

B Okay, how about a word game? Wanna play hangman?

A What?

B I asked if you want to play hangman.

A Are you kidding me?

B No. Why?

A That's a game from like a hundred, thousand, million years ago.

B So what?

A Abraham Lincoln probably played hangman when he was our age.

B Maybe that's why he was so smart.

A How do you know he was so smart?

B Because he never complained about being bored.

Clean Your Room

A Come on. Let's ride our bikes.

B No, I can't.

A Why not? Do you have company or something?

B No. I just can't go right now.

A Homework?

B Nah. Not really. Not too much.

A Do you have to study for a test?

B Nope.

A Just don't feel like it?

B No, I love to ride bikes. It's my most favorite thing.

A So, come on! Go get your bike and ride with me.

B I can't. I have to clean my stupid room!

A Says who?

B Says my mom. I've been putting it off, putting it off ...

A Yeah, but cleaning your room is a good thing. I always feel better when my room is all nice and clean and shiny.

B Yeah, I guess it would be good, but I'm just not so great at doing it.

A Tell you what, I'll come over and help.

B Really?!

A Yeah. I kinda like cleaning. I always help with the cleaning at home. With two of us cleaning, we'll finish your room quicker.

B   Maybe then we'll have time to ride our bikes.

A   Oh, yeah! That's what I'm talking about!

B   I know.

A   You do?

B   Yeah. You were just talking about it.

A Very Nice Invitation

A Did you understand what we did in math this morning?

B Yeah, kinda. Most of it, anyway.

A Well, I didn't understand any of it.

B Some of the exercises were a little … uh … convoluted.

A You mean tricky?

B Sorta tricky. They just had too many steps, but I'm gonna review it at home tonight.

A What do you mean "review it?"

B Oh, yeah. I'm checking over all the pages we did in class with my older sister. She's really good with math and science. She wants to be a math teacher someday. She's going to major in math in college.

A Why the heck would anybody want to do that?

B It's her best subject. She can do math in her sleep.

A Math *puts me* to sleep.

B I guess it just comes easier to her than most people.

A It sure doesn't come easily to me, I'll tell you that right now.

B If math won't come to you … then you come to it.

A What's that supposed to mean?

B It means you should study with us. Come over to our house.

A Really?

B Sure. Come over tonight. My sister will explain it to you. She'll explain it to me. We'll make it a two-for-one special.

A You don't think she'll mind? I don't want to bug her.

B Nah. I told you. She's gonna be a math teacher some day. It's probably good practice for her.

A That sounds terrific. Thanks. I'd love to.

B Stay for dinner. My dad's making his famous veggie pasta. It's really good, too. Almost edible.

Coloring Books, Milk, and Cookies

A   Wanna hear something funny?

B   No.

A   Good. I'm telling you anyway.

B   Thanks. I'll pretend I'm listening.

A   Remember my Uncle Joe?

B   The fireman.

A   No, that's Uncle Jack. This is my Uncle Joe, the teacher.

B   The one that teaches at the college, right?

A   That's him. My dad's older brother.

B   Way older brother.

A   C'mon, this is funny. Uncle Joe comes to visit. He brings me a couple of real nice coloring books. And he gets himself a book too. You know what kind?

B   Some boring history book probably. More stories from like a hundred, two hundred, five hundred years ago?

A   Wrong-o-matic. Guess again.

B   I don't know. A big, fat, boring book of maps?

A   Strike two.

B   A big, dusty book of boring poetry that nobody except college professors understands?

A   Not even close. Give up?

B   Give up.

A   A coloring book. He buys himself a coloring book.

B Come on. Stop joking.

A No joke. An adult coloring book.

B What's that about?

A He says grown-ups like coloring books now because their jobs are so hard.

B You mean too much stress?

A Yeah, so this helps them relax.

B Do a lot of grown-ups color?

A That's what I wanna know. They have all these special coloring books for grown-ups now.

B Did your dad get a coloring book too?

A No, but he kinda freaked about it.

B I don't blame him. His older brother.

A So he brought us milk and chocolate chip cookies.

B That's pretty funny.

A He said since we're both working so hard ... and since coloring is such important work ... his two favorite kids need a time-out. And a milk and cookie break.

B Works for me.

A I liked the cookies better than the coloring books.

B Right there with you, my friend.

A Tell me about it.

B I just did.

The History of Cupcakes

A Will you help me study for history?

B I don't like history.

A Really? I think it's so interesting.

B Not me. I think it's boring. Besides, I'm hungry. I want to go to lunch.

A But history has so many good stories.

B I don't think they're so good. Those old stories put me to sleep.

A They're great stories! I read about George Washington and Alexander Hamilton and Benjamin Franklin and all the other founding fathers.

B I wish the founding fathers found a way to be less boring.

A You're not being fair. You're not even giving history a chance.

B There's no future in history.

A C'mon. Help me study. Just for an hour.

B But I'm hungry! Hmmm … maybe if I have dessert first. And then lunch. Gotta be some cake or pie or ice cream around here someplace …

A I think every kid should learn world history.

B Boring! The most boring subject!

A And the history of their own country too.

B You know what kind of history I wanna learn?

A What?

B The history of cupcakes!

A I think cupcakes are boring.

B Not the way my mom makes them! She puts the "icious" in "delicious."

I Love The Zoo! I Hate The Zoo!

A My class is going to the zoo tomorrow!

B I hate the zoo.

A I love the zoo.

B Not me. I feel sorry for the animals. Locked up in a cage all day, every day.

A I know what you mean.

B It always makes me sad just thinking about them like that.

A I understand. We were talking about that in class. Our teacher did a whole lesson on the zoo.

B That's kinda cool. What did you learn?

A A lot. Believe it or not, we learned that animals in the zoo live longer than they do in the wild.

B Really?

A Yeah. I was surprised.

B I'm surprised too.

A Yeah, because they don't have other animals fighting with them and trying to eat them all the time.

B That kinda makes sense.

A They have animal doctors to take care of them if they get sick too.

B Veterinarians. I knew that part.

A So? Do you still hate the zoo?

B I don't know. I guess I have to think about it a little more.

A Thinking is always good.

B Yeah. A lot of people don't think enough.

A I think you're right.

B I think *you're* right!

Spiders Need Love Too!

A What are you working on?

B I'm writing a poem.

A Cool. About what?

B Spiders!

A Eeeeewwwww!! I hate spiders!

B I know. Everybody does.

A The whole wide world hates spiders!

B But we shouldn't. Don't hate them because they're different.

A I don't. I hate them because they're disgusting.

B It's not their fault they're scary and have eight legs. That's how nature made them.

A Well, nature made me hate spiders.

B My mother's afraid of them. She found a great big spider in the bathroom last night. You know what she did?

A Squished it?

B No, but she started screaming! My dad ran in and you know what he did?

A Squashed it?

B Nope. He picked him up on a napkin, took him outside, and set him free in the grass.

A So your dad actually saved that spider's life?

B Yep. He sure did.

A And now you're writing a poem about him?

B Yep. I sure am.

A Don't you think that's a little weird?

B Nope. Spiders need love too.

The Autobiography of Somebody Really Good

A What's that?

B A little story I'm writing.

A What's the title?

B The Autobiography of Somebody Really Good ... and Special.

A That's funny!

B Thanks.

A You're welcome. Who's your story about?

B C'mon, think about it. It's an autobiography. It's about me.

A Your autobiography?

B Yeah!

A But you're a kid! You're just a kid like I am!

B So what?

A You haven't been running around on this planet long enough to write an autobiography.

B Doesn't matter. My mom and dad say we have to change the way we speak to ourselves. We have to change the stories we believe about ourselves too.

A What the heck does that mean?

B It means too many people listen to the negative things people say to them all day long.

A Put-downs, you mean? Like insults?

B Sure, but not just that. People telling you all the stuff you can't do. What's not possible. You can't do this. You can't do that.

A I know what you mean. That kind of stuff is …

B Right. It gets in people's heads after a while. And then slowly, people start to actually believe all those awful, negative stories they've been hearing.

A So that's why your mom and dad say you have to change the stories you believe about yourself?

B Like changing the channel on the TV.

A Okay, I get it … but …

B Careful. Nothing negative now.

A Yeah, I get it. But … okay … how do I say this nicely … you're so young!

B Well, my autobiography doesn't have to be a whole book. Not yet. For now, it's just going to be a story. A nice, positive story.

A But you're not even in high school!

B A nice, positive, *short* story.

What Kind of Music Do You Like?

A Hey, do you want to hear some new music I got?

B Sure. Sounds like fun.

A Okay. What kind of music do you like?

B I like all different kinds, but country music is probably my favorite!

A Yuck! Sorry I even asked! That's cowboy music!

B No, not really. Country music has all kinds of good stories.

A What's good about them?

B I don't know. They're good stories about life, about all kinds of places you can visit. Country music makes me think of all the different places you can go.

A Yeah, but they're all Yo-Ho cowboy places.

B Not really. Besides, we shouldn't make fun of people just because they come from a different place, or because they like something different than we do. Even different music. That's almost like bullying.

A Oh, come on! That's not bullying.

B It's like you're judging people, though.

A I'm not judging.

B But you're making fun of people.

A Yeah, but ... but ...

B But what?

A I'm making fun of people I don't even know!

B And I'm just saying it's not nice to make fun of people.

A And they're Yo-Ho cowboy people. Come on! What's the big deal?

B I don't think it's very nice. You wouldn't like people making fun of you.

A But I never even met them!

B It's still not nice.

My Dad Lost His Job

A Have you been crying?

B Uh … yeah … a little.

A A little?

B A lot.

A What is it? Are you all right?

B It's not me. I'm worried about my dad.

A Is he feeling okay?

B He feels fine, but he got bad news at his work. He doesn't have a job any more.

A He got fired?

B Yesterday. Now him and my mom are all stressed out about how they're gonna pay for stuff.

A That's bad.

B I was up all night … trying to think how I can help …

A You can help make them feel better, but I think this is one of those things only grown-ups know what to do about.

B Gotta be some way I can help.

A There is. The best thing you can do is stop crying.

B That's not much help.

A It is to your dad. If you show him you're not worried, he'll know you believe in him.

B I guess that kinda makes sense.

A Then he'll have more confidence in himself.

B You mean like self-esteem?

A Exactly.

B Well ... maybe that can help him find another job.

A Sounds like a good way to help.

I'm Getting a New Little Brother or Sister!

A Guess what?

B What?

A My mom and dad are having a new baby!

B Hey, that's great! Are you excited?

A Of course! I'm gonna have a new little brother or sister, and I can teach them and help them with all kinds of stuff!

B Okay, good, because I saw on TV that a lot of kids feel kinda weird.

A Weird about what?

B I don't know. I think they start getting all jealous or something when their parents bring home a new baby.

A Yeah, but that's probably just rude, mean kids that don't understand anything about anything.

B I guess so.

A Mean kids get mad about all kinds of stupid stuff.

B You're probably right.

A Yeah. It's big, happy news for my whole family. Everything about it is good.

B Definitely.

A Too many people think about bad stuff all day long. We gotta focus on all the good stuff.

B   Sounds like you've got the right attitude.

A   Thanks a lot.

B   Your new little brother or sister is gonna be a pretty lucky kid.

A   Yeah, but you're just saying that because it's true.

B   It is true!

Don't Drink! Think!

A   My mom and dad showed me a video about drinking last night.

B   What kind of drinking?

A   The bad kind.

B   Like alcohol and stuff?

A   Exactly. The movie showed how dangerous drinking is.

B   I know some grown-ups get drunk. But why is it dangerous?

A   Because they don't know what they're doing.

B   Well … they know they're drinking.

A   That's all they know. They can't control themselves, so it gets dangerous.

B   You mean drinking and driving.

A   Sure, but even other stuff. When grown-ups drink too much, they can make bad mistakes at their work. And people can even get hurt.

B   So why do they do it?

A   My mom says people drink because they feel sad and lonely.

B   That's dumb!

A   I know!

B   If they get drunk and hurt someone, they'll be even sadder! And lonelier!

A They could even go to jail.

B I would hate to go to jail.

A Duh! Everyone hates going to jail!

B Don't be so sure. Maybe people do bad things and go to jail because it's the only place they feel comfortable.

A But it's horrible!

B It's horrible to us. But to them … maybe it feels like that's where they belong. Maybe it feels like going home.

A Well, I think drinking is stupid.

B Then why do so many grown-ups do it?

A Maybe they're not as grown up as they think.

B If they drink, they don't think.

No More Junk Food!

A Did you have lunch yet?

B Yeah. We had a good, healthy lunch at home.

A What kind of a healthy lunch?

B My dad made veggie burgers. We're eating a lot more vegetables at my house now. Big, giant, fluffy salads too. Yum. Yum. Yum.

A Hey, that almost sounds pretty good.

B My mom and dad are trying to eat healthier. They think it's a good idea for us kids to eat healthier too. No more junk food.

A Do you like it?

B Me and my brothers like it a lot. We're not drinking soda like we used to. We don't eat as many desserts either.

A Isn't it hard to give up dessert, though? That's my most favorite thing to eat.

B Well, we still have dessert sometimes. Just not every day.

A That's good.

B Yeah. And my parents make more healthy desserts now. With fruits and stuff.

A It sounds like you guys are definitely eating a lot healthier.

B I think it's good for us too. It feels like we all have a lot more energy now.

A Really? You can tell a difference?

B   Yeah. We're also not getting colds and headaches like we used to.

A   I'm gonna ask my parents if we can start eating healthy at my house.

B   Sounds good! Let me know when I can come over for a big, giant, fluffy salad.

New Technology

A Nice phone.

B Thanks.

A Is that new?

B Yeah. Present from my grandpa. Wasn't even my birthday or anything.

A My grandpa says technology changes so fast he can't ever keep up.

B These days.

A What?

B These days. Grandpa says things change so fast *these days* he can't keep up.

A That's funny. Yeah. That's exactly how my grandpa says it too. Things change so fast *these days.*

B Right, not like *those days.*

A Those days like when they were our age.

B Exactly. So this must be a pretty normal feeling ... a pretty common experience for people their age. They say it all the time, right?

A It must be kinda tough for them.

B Seeing so many changes.

A Email, cell phones, texting, computers, laptops.

B My grandpa says all that stuff is good, though.

A Mine says the same thing! Time marches on, and we all have to move forward.

B That's good. Our grandfathers both agree about the new technology.

A But he also says people don't talk anymore.

B They don't talk to each other like they did in his day.

A Those days. Like more friendly. Taking their time.

B He's right. It must be a big adjustment for people their age. Probably hard for them.

A So remember to call him on that new phone.

B I will.

A And talk to him nice and friendly. Not like you're in a hurry.

B Like they did back in those days.

Volunteer Work

A Where's your dad going? Is he working today?

B He's off from his job, but he's going to his volunteer job now.

A Volunteer? Really?

B I'm really proud of him. He volunteers every weekend.

A My dad says he won't do anything unless he gets paid.

B I think a lot of people probably feel that way.

A Yeah. He says there's only twenty-four hours in a day.

B That's the same thing my dad says! But he says it a little differently …

A How does he say it?

B My father says we all have the same number of hours. The average millionaire has the same twenty-four hours as the average homeless guy.

A So?

B What's important is how you use them.

A I get it. But millionaires can't be millionaires if they're always working for free.

B No, but they can donate a little time every week. They can volunteer for their favorite charities. Almost like spending time on a hobby.

A Yeah, I guess.

B Does your dad watch sports on the weekend?

A Sure. All day long.

B See? He can use some of that couch time for volunteering.

A I kinda don't think so.

B I bet his favorite sports stars do charity and volunteer work.

A That's different.

B Yeah, it's different. They're all millionaires.

A Long Car Ride

A Do you have a book I can borrow? Something good.

B Yeah. For what?

A We're taking a trip this weekend. It's a long car ride.

B Where to?

A To see my dad's cousins. Cousin Dana, her husband Tom, and their kids.

B Oh, I remember the pictures! Those kids are so cute!

A They're awesome. They live pretty far away. A long car ride.

B Why don't you bring a video game? You can play games on your phone too. Helps pass the time.

A I don't want to pass the time. I want to be productive.

B Then why don't you bring your homework?

A I don't want to be *that* productive!

B Pretty funny.

A Just kidding. I'm already caught up with schoolwork. Actually, I'm two chapters ahead.

B That's amazing. I wish I could be two chapters ahead.

A You can. You absolutely can. Nothing magical about it.

B Good idea. But it sounds kinda impossible.

A Nah. You just do a little bit extra every day.

B I guess that could probably work.

A It definitely works. That's why I want to start reading a new book. Get a jump on my summer list.

B What's your summer list?

A I started a list of books to read over summer break. I like to do extra reading. I don't always have time to do that when we're in school.

B That's another good idea.

A Yep. Just do a little bit extra every day.

B And I guess it all adds up, right?

A Yeah. And quicker than you think.

Do You Know What Winston Churchill Said?

A Do you know what Winston Churchill said?

B I don't even know who he is. How should I know what he said?

A He was supposed to be the greatest leader of the twentieth century. He said we should never give up. Never, ever give up.

B How did he say it?

A Never, ever give up! Sometimes he yelled it.

B Why did he yell it?

A To grab people's attention. Make sure they're listening.

B Yeah. Some people don't listen to anything. That's why they never learn anything.

A My dad says we should try to learn something new every day.

B Does your dad know Winston Churchill?

A No, no, no. Dad bought me this great book about him. Winston Churchill actually lived a long time ago. He was the Prime Minister of England.

B What's a Prime Minister?

A Leader of the country. Like a President.

B He was British?

A Yeah, but his mom was American, so that makes him half American too. My dad says the United States should get credit for half the good things he did.

B That's kinda funny.

A My dad's just joking around. He always does stuff like that. He tries to make learning new stuff fun.

B Does it work?

A You tell me. Here we are, two kids talking to each other about Winston Churchill instead of video games.

B That's true. What do you think your dad would say about that?

A Never, ever give up!

The Man In Black

A   Did you ever hear of a guy named Johnny Cash?

B   No. Did he invent money or something?

A   No, but he was probably pretty rich. He was a famous musician when he was alive.

B   He died?

A   Yeah. He died a few years ago.

B   What kind of music did he play?

A   Mostly country.

B   No. I don't like country cowboy music.

A   He played other kinds too. Rock. Gospel. He was a really good singer and musician. He wrote a lot of songs too. He started out with Elvis Presley.

B   Elvis was awesome. They called him "The King of Rock and Roll."

A   They called Johnny Cash "The Man in Black."

B   What for? Did he always wear a black hat or something?

A   Not just the hat. He wore black everything. He always wore all black.

B   That's pretty cool. But it would be kinda boring to wear the same color every day.

A   But there was a reason he wore black. The reason was definitely not boring.

B   What's the reason?

A He said he would always wear black for the people who had no hope. And for the people who didn't have enough money or even enough food to eat.

B So it's like he was making a personal sacrifice or something.

A Yeah. He was doing it for other people. He wanted to see a happier and more beautiful world.

B So what happened?

A He always wore the black, up until the day he died. There's still poor people. We all know that.

B It's kinda sad that he never saw things turn around for the people he was singing for. The people with no money. The ones with no hope.

A But it's kinda inspiring too. It's amazing that a big famous musician would decide to do something like that for all those millions of people he never met.

B And it makes me think about what kids can do.

A Like who?

B Like you and me.

A Like maybe we can do something to make the world a better place too?

B Yeah, why not? Or at least make our own little corner of the world a better place.

North to Alaska

A Remember that exercise we did in class last week?

B Which one?

A The one we worked on with the sub.

B I think so. That substitute teacher always gives us cool lessons.

A The one where had to write a list of goals and things we wanna do.

B That was the best lesson! Everybody should write a list like that. It gives you stuff to think about.

A Good stuff instead of junky stuff.

B Right, right, right.

A I've been adding to that list at home all week.

B You mean writing even more goals?

A Yeah, and I came up with some I really like.

B So? Tell me! Tell me!

A Okay, this is great! I think it's great, anyway. I want to go to all fifty states.

B In the U.S.?

A Of course in the U.S.!

B How many have you been to already?

A I started writing them down. I got to seven.

B Seven's pretty good. That's a lot.

A How about you?

B Not sure. I don't think as many as you. Maybe four, five, something like that.

A Four or five is good. You know what's really cool, though? I started thinking which states are the ones I want to see the most.

B Which ones did you pick?

A Ready?

B Ready.

A Our forty-ninth state. Alaska.

B Alaska?! But it's so cold!

A Not in the summertime!

B Does it get hot in the summer?

A Not hot, just normal, like where we live.

B But why Alaska?

A Because probably not too many people would even think about going there.

B Most people would pick California or Hawaii, right?

A Or Florida. Someplace warm.

B That makes sense.

A I even went online and looked up all kinds of information on Alaska.

B Cool. Alaska's like the girl nobody thinks of asking for a date! But you asked her!

A   Yeah! From now on, I'm calling Alaska the unsung hero of the United States!

B   That's pretty funny.

A   Maybe I'll do a report on Alaska too. I found a lot of interesting trivia and stuff.

B   That substitute is amazing. She always has like a million, billion fun things for us to work on in class. Wish we did more stuff like that with our regular teacher.

Shorter Scenes
for Younger Actors

These next few scenes are a bit shorter, and will be a little easier for younger students to memorize. There's another twist written into these scenes, as well. Actors have an opportunity to add a couple of additional lines of dialogue to the endings. This is a nice challenge that adds an extra element of difficulty to these shorter scenes. Adding your own lines to the end of a scene is an effective test of our creativity, and helps actors (of all ages) develop improvisational skills. Have fun with these scenes and be as creative as possible. You can do it.

Cafeteria

A Did you eat lunch in the cafeteria?

B Yes. It was just awful today!

A It sure was! It was horrible!

B Yeah! Disgusting!

A Oh, and it smelled bad too . . . I don't think it was fresh hamburger . . .

B Hamburger? I thought it was chicken!

A Chicken? No way! It was too smelly!

B It must have been old lamb chops!

A No! Maybe it was stinky fish sticks!

B Yuck! I don't feel so good ...

A _____

B _____

Peanut Butter and Jelly

A   Do you want to trade sandwiches?

B   What kind do you have?

A   Peanut butter and jelly.

B   Grape jelly?

A   No . . .

B   What kind?

A   Strawberry.

B   Hmmmmmm . . . with chunks?

A   No. No chunks of strawberry. It's smooth. Very smooth.

B   How about the peanut butter? Smooth or bumpy?

A   Chunky.

B   Okay! I'll trade! I like smooth jelly and bumpy peanut butter!

A   _____

B   _____

New In School

A Do you know the way to the bus stop?

B I think so.

A You think so or you know so?

B I think I know so. I'm new here.

A Me too! This is my first day.

B Do you like it?

A I guess so. Except for all the woodpeckers!

B Woodpeckers? Really?

A Yeah. Do you have woodpeckers in your classroom?

B No. We have penguins.

A Wow. You're lucky.

B Yeah, except we have to keep our classroom really cold.

A _____

B _____

Flip Flops or Sneakers?

A Why do you always wear flip flops?

B I love my flip flops. They're so comfortable.

A But sneakers are better for running and playing.

B Nah. I like the sound my flip flops make when I walk. Flip, flop. Flip, flop. Flip, flop.

A That's cool. But I still like sneakers.

B Sneakers are sweaty!

A Sneakers are awesome!

B But sneakers don't even make any kind of noise!

A I know! That's the whole idea! They're quiet so you can sneak around!

B Ooooh! That's why they're called sneakers! They're good for sneaking!

A Yeah, so you can walk around on tippy-toe and nobody will hear you!

B Too bad they don't make sneaky flip flops!

A _____

B _____

The Principal's Office

A Do you know the way to the Principal's office?

B Oh, no! Are you in trouble?

A No. I don't think so.

B But only kids who are in trouble have to go to the Principal's office!

A Don't worry. Just point me to the Principal's office. Which way? This way? That way? Upstairs? Downstairs?

B Down this hall. I'm going with you too. Maybe you'll need help

A I don't need help eating lunch!

B Lunch? You're eating lunch in the Principal's office?

A Yeah. She made my lunch for me.

B Yeah, right! Don't eat in her office! You're gonna get in trouble!

A No, I won't. The Principal is also my mom!

B Oh! I get it now!

A _____

B _____

Saving Money

A Wanna go to the store with me? I just got my allowance.

B Okay, but I'm not spending any money. But I'll keep you company.

A You sure? I think they just got the new comic books.

B Very sure. I'm saving my money.

A What for?

B I want to get a new bike.

A But you have a nice bike.

B Yeah, but I'm probably gonna want a new one sometime next year.

A Next ... year? That's so far away!

B Exactly! So if I start saving money now, I'll be ready to buy anything I want later on.

A But if you save money now ... you can't buy stuff you like now.

B But I can buy stuff I like better later.

A _____

B _____

Afterword

I'd like to leave you with a great little piece of advice. Always do more than is expected of you. This is commonly called "going the extra mile."

Don't be the person who does as little as possible. Don't be the one who just tries to squeak by. We have enough people like that running around loose already.

We need more people who always do their best. We need more "100 per cent" people in this world. Wake up each day and decide you're going to do your best, be your best, and try your best to make a genuine difference on this funny little planet of ours.

If you want to live in a better world, then make up your mind to be a better person yourself. You don't have to be perfect. You never have to be perfect. You just have to make a decision to become the best possible version of yourself. This is a very important daily discipline for actors.

And make sure you're extra nice to mom and dad. Remember that every day is Canadian Mother's Day and Australian Father's Day.

Thanks for reading all the way to the end too. I'm proud of you.

A Bold and Humble Request

If you've enjoyed this book – and believe it will benefit young actors and their teachers – I hope you'll indulge this bold and humble request.

It's very important for new authors to spread the word about books they've written in a variety of different ways. Everybody needs a little help with something, and people who write books are no exception. There are many things that help books reach a wider audience, and all of them add up over time.

Please consider taking a few minutes to assist in one or more of these areas:

– Tell your friends about this book, and our companion book for teenagers, *Scenes for Teens*.

– Post a message out on your favorite social media platform or book-related website. Facebook, Twitter, Pinterest, Instagram, Amazon, Barnes & Noble, Goodreads, and YouTube are all terrific resources for writers and readers.

– Recommend this book (and *Scenes for Teens*) to your school library and local public library. Schools and libraries can often buy books at a significant discount. This will also assist aspiring young actors whose families may not be able to purchase their own copies.

Each of these action steps is extremely helpful. Together, they really do add up and make a difference. Thank you sincerely, dear readers, for purchasing this book, and for all your support.

About the Author

Mike Kimmel is a film, television, stage, and commercial actor and acting coach. He is a twenty-plus year member of SAG-AFTRA with extensive experience in both the New York and Los Angeles markets. He has worked with directors Francis Ford Coppola, Robert Townsend, Craig Shapiro, and Christopher Cain. TV credits include *Game of Silence, Zoo, Treme, In Plain Sight, Cold Case, Breakout Kings, Memphis Beat,* and *Buffy the Vampire Slayer.* He was a regular sketch comedy player on *The Tonight Show,* performing live on stage and in pre-taped segments with Jay Leno for eleven years.

Mike has appeared in dozens of theatrical plays on both coasts, including Radio City Music Hall, Equity Library Theater, Stella Adler Theater, and Theater at the Improv. He trained with Michael Shurtleff, William Hickey, Ralph Marrero, Gloria Maddox, Harold Sylvester, Wendy Davis, Amy Hunter, Bob Collier, and Stuart Robinson. He has a B.A. from Brandeis University and an M.A. from California State University.

As an educator and lecturer, he has taught at Upper Iowa University, University of New Orleans, University of Phoenix, Nunez Community College, Delgado Community College, and in both the Los Angeles and Beverly Hills school districts. He is a two-time past president of New Orleans Toastmasters, the public speaking organization, and often serves as a speech contest judge. Mike has written and collaborated on numerous scripts for stage and screen. His full-length historical drama on Presidents Lincoln and Garfield was a 2013 semifinalist in the National Playwrights Conference at the Eugene O'Neill Theater Center. He is the 2014 recipient of the Excellence in Teaching Award from Upper Iowa University.

Recommended Reading
for Kids and Parents

Acting in Film by Michael Caine

Audition by Michael Shurtleff

Audition and Book It! by Helen McCready

How to Act & Eat at the Same Time by Tom Logan

How to Audition on Camera by Sharon Bialy

Know Small Parts by Laura Cayouette

Letters to a Young Actor by Robert Brustein

Letters to a Young Artist by Anna Deavere Smith

100 Ways to Motivate Yourself by Steve Chandler

Scenes for Teens by Mike Kimmel

The Courage to Create by Rollo May

"How wonderful it is that nobody need wait a single moment before starting to improve the world."

– Anne Frank

CPSIA information can be obtained
at www.ICGtesting.com
Printed in the USA
LVHW021633241118
598147LV00010B/76/P